THE WINDOW

For my two grandfathers: Henry Preiss and Dudley Chamberlain. ~ L G

For Dondok, the grandad I never got to meet. And for Polina, Raquel and Pepe, the most wonderful grandparents I could have had. ~ U L

A STUDIO PRESS BOOK

First published in the UK in 2022 by Studio Press Books,
an imprint of Bonnier Books UK,
4th Floor, Victoria House, Bloomsbury Square, London WC1B 4DA
Owned by Bonnier Books,
Sveavägen 56, Stockholm, Sweden

www.bonnierbooks.co.uk

ISBN 978-1-78741-983-4

Edited by Frankie Jones and Emma Drage
Designed by Nia Williams
Production by Emma Kidd

A CIP catalogue for this book is available from the British Library
Printed and bound in China

THE WINDOW

By Laura Gehl

Illustrated by Udayana Lugo

STUDIO PRESS

Daria's grandpa had a window that looked out at the ocean.

Most of the windows at the hospital looked out onto dull, grey buildings.

But Daria's grandpa could see
the ocean every day.

Each time Daria visited, she held Grandpa's hand, and they looked out the window together.

They saw waves crashing.

Families swimming.

Kites flying.

"We'll fly kites when you get better. Right, Grandpa?"

"Of course we will."

Some days, they saw seagulls flying near puffy white clouds.
Other days, colourful sunsets.

And once – even a rainbow.

"We'll look for the pot of gold at the end of the rainbow when you get better. Right, Grandpa?"

"Right, sweetie."

One day, Grandpa was too weak
to move to a chair. But Daria
helped him sit up in bed and
look out the window.

"See that little girl and her grandpa
building a sandcastle?" Daria said.
"They look like us, don't they?"

Grandpa had an oxygen mask now to help him breathe. He couldn't talk with the mask on, but he nodded, and his eyes smiled at Daria.

"We're going to build the biggest sandcastle in the world when you get better. Right, Grandpa?"

Grandpa squeezed her hand. Not very tight, but tight enough. Daria knew the squeeze meant yes.

The next time Daddy went
to the hospital, he asked if
Daria wanted to stay home.
He said Daria could make
Grandpa a card instead.

But Daria wanted to go.

Daria and Grandpa looked out
the window at the storm.

Grey skies.

Pounding rain.

Lightning.

Grandpa squeezed Daria's hand.
Not very tight, but tight enough.
This time, Daria knew the squeeze
meant "I love you". Daria squeezed back.

Daria went with Daddy
to bring home Grandpa's
things from the hospital.

Daddy carried Grandpa's
books and glasses.

Daria carried
Grandpa's window.

Daria's window looked out at the ocean.

Most of the windows in Daria's apartment
looked out onto dull, grey buildings.

But Daria could see the ocean every day.

And when she looked out the window, Daria could feel Grandpa's hand squeezing hers. Not very tight, but tight enough.

For all of us, and especially for a child, saying goodbye for ever feels hard to do. It can be difficult to understand what's happening and what death means.

Children will show a wide range of feelings and behaviours during and after a time of loss. They might be sad and want a cuddle or quiet comfort, act as if nothing's happened or they've forgotten, or you might see angry or naughty behaviour and regression to younger ways of talking and acting. Whatever you see, remember that they'll need your support and it's important to keep talking about and remembering their loved one. They might have questions to ask or simply feel lost and confused. The most important thing is that they are helped to explore their feelings and make sense of what's happened.

Use clear language like, 'Grandpa has died', instead of metaphors. Saying Grandpa's 'sleeping' or 'in the next room' can be frightening and too abstract for a child to make meaning from.

Be honest if they ask whether their loved one is coming back. Say something like, 'No, but we will always remember the special times we had with them.'

Read and talk about stories like this one together. Children don't have to understand death straight away or all at once. It will gradually make sense over time.

Children often believe they've caused things to happen because of something they did, said or thought. However obvious it seems, reassure them that nothing they did caused this and nothing they could've done would have prevented it.

Remind them it's okay to be sad and it's equally okay not to be sad. Their feelings will naturally come and go. Their loved one would want them to be happy and have lots of fun again.

Set up a memory box or, just like Daria did, draw and put up lots of pictures of special memories they shared with their loved one. Celebrate them and remember that it still matters they shared that love.

Grief might bubble up at unexpected times and anniversaries. There's no 'right' amount of time for grief. If you feel that your child isn't coming to terms with their loss, you can always seek expert advice and guidance.

Look after yourself – you are grieving as well. Turn to your own support network for comfort or contact one of the organisations listed.

Dr Sharie Coombes

Organisations that can offer support for you and your child:

Child Bereavement UK
Free online chat: www.childbereavementuk.org
Monday to Friday, 9 a.m. – 5 p.m.
Helpline: 0800 02 888 40, Monday to Friday, 9 a.m. – 5 p.m.

Winston's Wish
Crisis Messenger: 24/7, text WW to 85258
Free online chat: www.winstonswish.org
Mondays 1 p.m. – 5 p.m. and Fridays 9.30 a.m. – 1 p.m.
Helpline: 08088 020 021, Monday to Friday, 9 a.m. - 5 p.m.

Sue Ryder
Free online professional bereavement support and support community:
www.sueryder.org